TAKE THAT

THE CIRCUS

TAKE THAT

THE CIRCUS

WISE PUBLICATIONS
part of The Music Sales Group
London/New York/Paris/Sydney/Copenhagen/Berlin/Madrid/Tokyo

Published by
Wise Publications
14-15 Berners Street, London W1T 3LJ, UK.

Exclusive distributors:
Music Sales Limited
Distribution Centre, Newmarket Road,
Bury St Edmunds, Suffolk IP33 3YB, UK.

Music Sales Pty Limited
20 Resolution Drive, Caringbah, NSW 2229, Australia.

Order No. AM996677
ISBN 978-1-84772-957-6

Edited by Jenni Wheeler.

Photography: Rick Guest.
Original CD Sleeve Design & Art Direction: Studio Fury.

Printed in the EU.

THE GARDEN

Words & Music by Mark Owen, Gary Barlow, Jason Orange & Howard Donald

HELLO

Words & Music by Mark Owen, Gary Barlow, Stephen Robson,
Jason Orange & Howard Donald

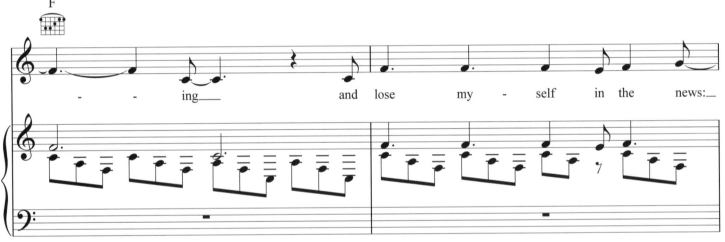

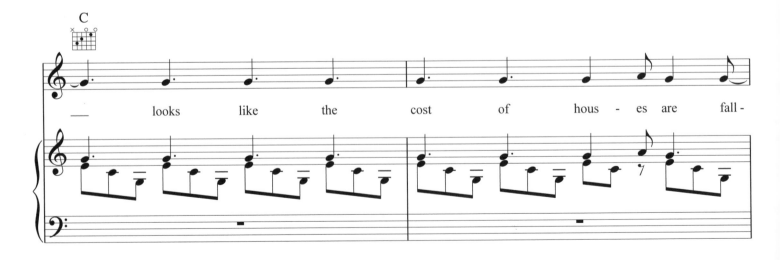

1.

Bb

2. I'd lock my - self a - way in the ev -

F

- - 'ning, a - fraid to ev - er come out__

C

__ watch T. - V. and get lost in my feel-

G   G#

- - ings, feel - - ings._____

19

20

SAID IT ALL

Words & Music by Mark Owen, Gary Barlow, Stephen Robson,
Jason Orange & Howard Donald

GREATEST DAY

Words & Music by Mark Owen, Gary Barlow, Jason Orange & Howard Donald

Original key D♭ major

♩ = 112

To-day this could be the great-est day of our lives.

Be-fore it all ends, be-fore we run out of time. Stay

29

31

JULIE

Words & Music by Mark Owen, Gary Barlow, Stephen Robson,
Jason Orange & Howard Donald

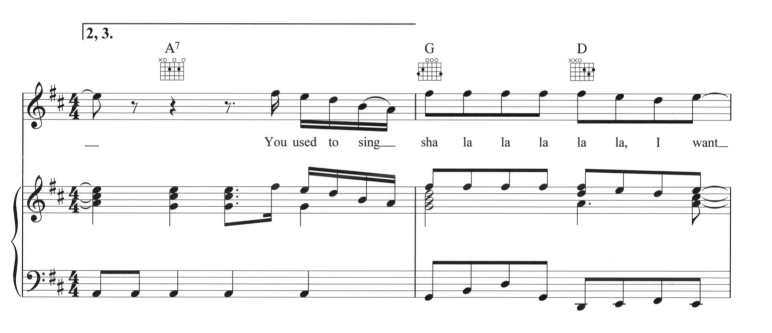

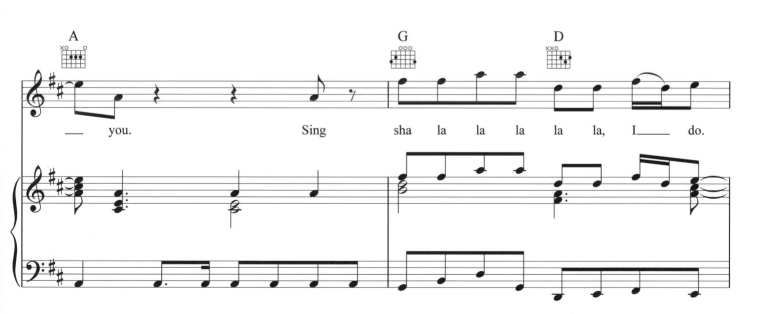

THE CIRCUS

Words & Music by Mark Owen, Gary Barlow, Jason Orange & Howard Donald

2. Stand up, please, till I'm done los - ing my mind, and I've
3. Si - lence, please, 'cause I've got some-thing to say, and be -

thanked you all just one too man - y times; the
-fore the mu - sic takes you all a - way: I

more we fall, the hard - er we must climb, now that you're
(3, 4.) nev - er thought I'd leave it all so late, now that you're

gone, now that you're gone. 'Cause
gone, oh,___ you're gone. Yeah,

41

ev - 'ry - bod - y loves a cir - cus show, but I'm the on - ly clown you'll ev - er

know; and now you can ap - plaud my best mis - take: "I

To Coda ⊕

love you" was too man - y words to say, to

say. say, "I

43

HOW DID IT COME TO THIS

Words & Music by Mark Owen, Gary Barlow, Jason Orange, Howard Donald, Ben Mark & Jamie Norton

slight-ly schiz-o-phren-ic and a   lit-tle out of reach my friend."   I said "Yes, that's part-ly true but

jokes a-side I can ex-plain, it's   just my way of keep-ing track with   liv-ing on this plan-et." Now then,

G

Gmaj⁷

have   you   turned   on   your   T.   V.?   Have   you   seen   re - al - i - ty?
2. All   this   noise   and   all   these   lights,   all   this   talk - ing   through   the   night,

C/G

Have   you   found   the   pro - gram   that   you   spent   your   whole   life   look - ing   for?
all   this   ex - pec - ta - tion   now,   it's   mak - ing   me   neu - ro - tic.   Tell   me,

There's a girl in Cam-den Town, in-de-ci-sion makes her frown.
have I seen your face be-fore? I for-got to say hel-lo.

Which dress would she wear to-day and which way should she smile at me?
Thought I'd make it clear now that I've al-ways been a smi-ler. Tell me...

How did it come_ to this?_____ How_ did_ it ev-

-er come_ to_____ this._____

it's like__ I'm a world__ a-way. Some-times I feel a world_ a-way.__

3. Just the oth-er day some-bod-y said to me "Hey, may-be you are

oh, so slight-ly O. C. D. a lit-tle out of reach my friend."

I said "Yes, that's part-ly true but jokes a-side, please stay with me. It's

D.S. al Coda

just my way of com-part-men-tal - is - ing all the things I see."

Coda

- er come_ to_____ this._____

G

Gmaj⁷

G⁶

Gsus⁴

G

UP ALL NIGHT

Words & Music by Mark Owen, Gary Barlow, Jason Orange, Howard Donald,
Ben Mark & Jamie Norton

times it cuts me up, think-ing of___ you. All the hope I've
3. Pour an-oth-er glass while I watch___ the bot-tle dis-ap-

got, wast-ed on___ you. All the talks we
-pear. While I watch___ the morn-ing light ap-

had nev-er did___ no___ good. }
-pear think-ing a-bout___ you. }

Oh,___

may-be___ I don't need you to save___ me.___ I just want you to help___

51

YOU

Words & Music by Mark Owen, Gary Barlow, Jason Orange & Howard Donald

1. It's not a spark that gives me light.

It's not the days I'm up all night.__ Is - n't a sto - ry

57

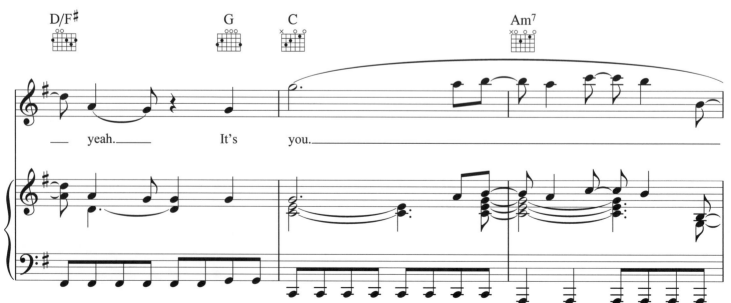

WHAT IS LOVE

Words & Music by Mark Owen, Gary Barlow, Jason Orange & Howard Donald

61

HOLD UP A LIGHT

Words & Music by Mark Owen, Gary Barlow, Jason Orange, Howard Donald, Ben Mark & Jamie Norton

hold up a light.＿ Hold up a light＿ for me, hold up＿ a light.＿

A light＿＿＿＿＿＿＿＿ for me.＿

I'll be watch - ing

you. I'll be watch - ing you.＿

SHE SAID

Words & Music by Mark Owen, Gary Barlow, Jason Orange & Howard Donald

1. (𝄋)My love was filled with trou-ble, with in-de-

2. My love, as bad as fast food. As low as

73

said she want-ed a good___ time. Girl,___ I think I love you.___

Shake it.___ Ev - 'ry-bod- y now, shake it.___ Ev - 'ry-bod- y just

step to the right, jump up, turn a-round and shake it.___ Ev - 'ry-bod- y now,

boo - gie.___ Ev - 'ry-bod- y now, boo - gie.___ Ev - 'ry-bod- y put your

74

HERE

Words & Music by Mark Owen, Gary Barlow, Olly Knights, Gale Paridjanian,
Jason Orange & Howard Donald

2 3 4 5 6 7 8 9
8/09(170573)